LOCKDOWN
HAIR

By Linda Steinbock
Illustrations by Alexandra Rusu

Printed in the United States of America

ISBN 978-1-953910-19-6 (hardcover)
ISBN 978-1-953910-20-2 (paperback)
ISBN 978-1-953910-21-9 (ebook)

Canoe Tree Press
4697 Main Street
Manchester Center, VT 05255

Canoe Tree Press is a division of DartFrog Books.

To all those willing to sacrifice their own safety in this global crisis, I dedicate this book in your honour. I hope it brings light to you and your family.

And to my husband Seán, with hope in our hearts, we'll never walk alone.

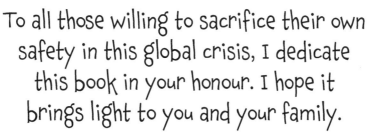

Siona is with her family, listening to the President address the nation...

"...Thank you for keeping your family and community safe by social distancing and wearing face masks. This will help prevent the spread of Coronavirus."

"Siona, sweetie, you seem distracted," Mum says with concern. "Is there something on your mind?"

Tears fill Siona's eyes. "I miss Granny!"

"Well," Dad says, "it's sad we can't visit Granny because we're in lockdown. But that doesn't mean we can't **SEE** her."

Siona thinks for a moment. Then her face breaks into a huge smile. "We can **CALL** her!"

"Ahhh!" Siona shrieks. "Granny, what **EVER** happened to your hair?"

Granny laughs. "I know, my dear, I'm in desperate need of a haircut. But all the salons are closed!"

"My clients call all the time, asking me to cut their hair, but I can't because of government health regulations," Mum explains.

"I thought the pandemic would all be over in a few weeks. Now I wonder if things will ever be normal again," Granny sighs.

"Don't worry," Mum says lovingly. "When the salon opens again, you will be my first customer. Although, it won't be quite like it was before. We can only open when we have proper health and safety measures. But we will manage."

"We **HAVE** to! Have you seen what some people have done to their own hair?"

"What sort of safety measures, Mum?"
Siona asks curiously.

"Well, we normally stand really close to our clients to cut their hair, so we'll have to wear masks and gloves to protect ourselves and our clients. But I'm sure we could do a few other things to be even safer."

"What about making sure you have hand sanitizer and masks available?" Granny suggests.

"Yes," Mum says, "I'm sure we'll have to do that. Though it might be best if people bring their own masks."

"Those are great ideas!" Siona says.
"I must go and think of some more. I'll
talk to you later, Granny. I love you!"

"I love you too, pumpkin,"
Granny says, "and I miss you
like crazy. I have so many hugs
and kisses saved up for you!"

Siona runs up to her room,
full of excitement. She sits at her
desk and focuses her mind.

Last year, she visited Mum at the
salon on Bring Your Daughter to Work
Day. Siona was fascinated to see
all the things Mum did at work.

Can she remember them all?

1. Ask client what she wants
2. Comb hair
3. Shampoo hair
4. Wash hair
5. Cut hair
6. Blow dry hair

Siona feels really proud of herself for remembering all the steps in Mum's job.

The President said we need to keep two metres apart from each other. She called it "social distancing." How on earth can Mum do that in her salon? How can you possibly wash or cut someone's hair if they're two metres away from you?

"Of course!" she cries. **"I'VE GOT IT!"**

And Siona gets to work.

Step 1: ask client what she wants.

"Now this is going to be interesting," Siona says. "From the tip of her toes to the top of her head, Mum's whole body isn't two metres long. So, her arms will be too short to wash or cut hair.

Let me think..."

Step 2: comb hair.

"I can't wait for Mum to try this," Siona says. "I just know it will work!"

Step 3: shampoo hair.

"The best part of a haircut is a head massage," Siona says, closing her eyes and rubbing her forehead.

"But we can't do that during the pandemic, so the client will have to massage their own head.

"Gosh, this is genius," Siona shouts. "Isn't it amazing? When you really need to help someone and you put your mind to it, good ideas come to you.

"That part is done. Now what?"

Step 4: wash hair.

"No worries, that's easy enough," Siona says.
"Mum has the bucket right there...

...Yeah! She looks happy.

It's going great, but now for the main event..."

Step 5: cut hair.

"Ooh! Mind her ears, Mum!

It's looking pretty good! And now, we need to dry her hair. But how will we do that...?"

Step 6: blow-dry hair.

Siona giggles.
"Oh, Mum, you are so creative!"

"Mum, look what I made for you! It's a step-by-step guide to keep you safe when you go back to work!"

Siona, this is brilliant!" Mum says proudly. "I'll need to show this to all my friends at the hair salon! We'll definitely keep everyone safe if we do haircuts like this!"

Dad hugs Siona. "You're going to be an inventor when you grow up!"

"I'm an inventor NOW," Siona says confidently. "Mum, I'm so happy you can use these ideas when the salon opens again. But maybe...

...you can start with **MY** hair first!"

"No one is too small
to make a difference."

Greta Thunberg

Discussion and comprehension

Discuss the story with the children and ask the following questions encouraging them to take turns and share their thoughts.

Offer support by turning to the relevant pages of the book if needed.

- Can you remember the six hairdressing steps and the ideas Siona had to keep her mum safe?

- Why was Siona shocked to see her Grandma's hair?

- Can you think of a time when you felt sad or worried about the virus? Is there anything you'd like to share with me that we can solve together?

- How many face masks can you find in the story?

- Based on the story, can you remember the different ways to stay safe?

ABOUT THE AUTHOR

Linda Steinbock is a humanitarian aid worker of Swedish and Malay-Singaporean descent. She attended university in Melbourne, Australia and began working for an NGO, supporting children and families affected by conflict, typhoons, earthquakes and tsunamis. Her work also involved research into how children are affected by crisis, never more so than during the Covid-19 pandemic.

It was while quarantined in Singapore that Linda came up with the idea of a children's picture book which illustrates how the power of human connection can overcome adversity, and how even distanced relationships can continue to lift us up during these anxious times.

Through her book and her website, Linda hopes to create a space where others can share how they've overcome isolation and enhanced connection with those they love, and to foster discussion about long distance, multi-cultural friendships and relationships. Come join the conversation at lindasteinbock.com, where you can also find teacher resources and activity sheets for **Lockdown Hair**.

Lightning Source UK Ltd.
Milton Keynes UK
UKHW050449101021
391884UK00005B/39